Editor
Lorin E. Klistoff, M.A.

Managing Editor
Karen Goldfluss, M.S. Ed.

Cover Artist
Barb Lorseyedi

Art Manager
Kevin Barnes

Art Director
CJae Froshay

Imaging
James Edward Grace
Rosa C. See

Publisher
Mary D. Smith, M.S. Ed.

Author

Mary Rosenberg

Teacher Created Resources, Inc.
6421 Industry Way
Westminster, CA 92683
www.teachercreated.com

ISBN-1-4206-8600-3

©2005 Teacher Created Resources, Inc.
Made in U.S.A.

Table of Contents

Introduction

The old adage "practice makes perfect" can really hold true for your child and his or her education. The more practice and exposure your child has to concepts being taught in school, the more success he or she is likely to find. For many parents, knowing how to help your children can be frustrating because the resources may not be readily available. As a parent, it is also difficult to know where to focus your efforts so that the extra practice your child receives at home supports what he or she is learning in school.

This book has been designed to help parents and teachers reinforce basic skills with their children. *Practice Makes Perfect* reviews basic math skills for children in grade 4. The math focus is on geometry. While it would be impossible to include all concepts taught in grade 4 in this book, the following basic objectives are reinforced through practice exercises. These objectives support math standards established on a district, state, or national level. (Refer to the Table of Contents for the specific objectives of each practice page.)

- identifying and naming plane and solid figures
- identifying and naming parallel, intersecting, and perpendicular lines
- parts of a circle
- congruent figures
- symmetry

- angles
- identifying and naming parts of a solid figure
- identifying triangles based on angles or sides
- identifying quadrilaterals based upon their sides and angles

There are 37 practice pages organized sequentially, so children can build their knowledge from more basic skills to higher-level math skills. (**Note:** Have children show all work where computation is necessary to solve a problem. For multiple-choice responses on practice pages, children can fill in the letter choice or circle the answer.) Following the practice page are six test practices. These provide children with multiple-choice test items to help prepare them for standardized tests administered in schools. To correct the test pages and the practice pages in this book, use the answer key provided on pages 47 and 48.

How to Make the Most of This Book

Here are some useful ideas for optimizing the practice pages in this book:

- Set aside a specific place in your home to work on the practice pages. Keep it neat and tidy with materials on hand.
- Set up a certain time of day to work on the practice pages. This will establish consistency. An alternative is to look for times in your day or week that are less hectic and conducive to practicing skills.
- Keep all practice sessions with your child positive and constructive. If the mood becomes tense or you and your child are frustrated, set the book aside and look for another time to practice with your child.
- Help with instructions if necessary. If your child is having difficulty understanding what to do or how to get started, work through the first problem with him or her.
- Review the work your child has done. This serves as reinforcement and provides further practices.
- Pay attention to the areas in which your child has the most difficulty. Provide extra guidance and exercises in those areas. Allowing children to use drawings and manipulatives, such as coins, tiles, game markers, or flash cards, can help them grasp difficult concepts more easily.
- Look for ways to make real-life applications to the skills being reinforced.

Practice 1

Plane Shapes and Solid Shapes

A **plane** shape is a shape that is flat and two dimensional. A **solid** shape is three dimensional. It has sides and a top and bottom.

Directions: Match each plane shape to its solid form.

1.

square

triangle

circle

rectangle

sphere

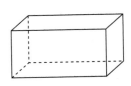

rectangular prism

triangular pyramid

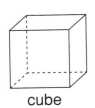

cube

Directions: Look at each solid shape. What plane figures do you see on its flat surfaces? Outline the plane figures. Write the name(s) of the plane figure(s) on the line(s).

2. rectangular prism

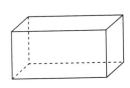

_____

and _____

3. rectangular pyramid

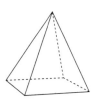

_____

and _____

4. cube

_____

5. cylinder

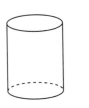

_____

6. cone

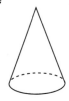

_____

7. triangular pyramid

_____

Practice 2

Solid Shapes

Directions: Write the name of the solid shape that matches each item.

cylinder	cone	rectangular prism	pyramid	sphere

1.

_____

2.

_____

3.

_____

4.

_____

5.

_____

6.

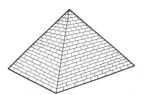

_____

7.

_____

8.

_____

9.

_____

10. Can you think of other items that are shaped like a cylinder? _____

_____

Solid Patterns

Directions: Which solid figure would each pattern make?

cone	rectangular prism	rectangular pyramid
cylinder	cube	triangular pyramid

1.

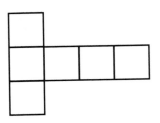

_____

2.

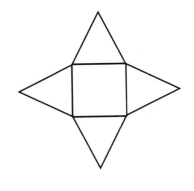

_____

3.

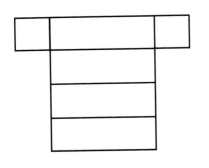

_____

4.

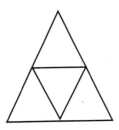

_____

5.

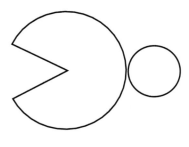

_____

6.

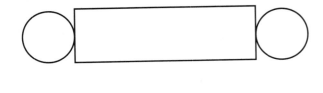

_____

Practice 4

Quadrilaterals: Squares and Rectangles

Square: All four sides are *equal* (or the same length) and all angles are 90°.

Rectangle: Opposite sides are *congruent* (exactly the same) and all angles are 90°.

Directions: Name each quadrilateral. Use single and/or double hash marks to identify opposite sides that are congruent.

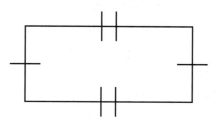

— Set or opposite sides that are congruent.

  Set or opposite sides that are congruent.

1.

_____

2.
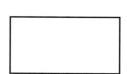

_____

3.

_____

4.
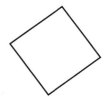

_____

5.
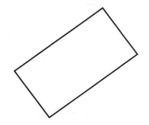

_____

6.

_____

7. How are a square and a rectangle alike? _____

_____

8. How are a square and a rectangle different? _____

_____

Practice 5

Quadrilaterals: Other Shapes with Four Sides and Four Angles

Parallelogram: Opposite sides are congruent and parallel.

Rhombus: All four sides are congruent, opposite sides are parallel.

Trapezoid: Only one pair of parallel sides.

Directions: Parallel lines are lines that run next to each other without crossing. Circle the sets of parallel lines.

1.

2.

3.
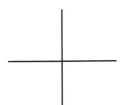

4.

Directions: Name each quadrilateral. Use hash marks to identify parallel sides.

5.
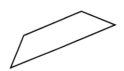

_____

6.
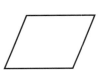

_____

7.

_____

8.
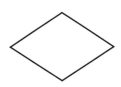

_____

9.
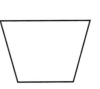

_____

10.
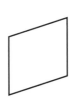

_____

11. How are a trapezoid and a rectangle alike?_____

_____

12. How are a trapezoid and a rectangle different?_____

_____

Practice 6

Polygons

Polygons (*poly* = many, *gons* = angles) are shapes with many angles.		
penta = five	hepta = seven	nona = nine
hexa = six	octa = eight	deca = ten

Directions: An angle is formed where two sides meet. Count the number of angles. Write the complete name of each shape on the line.

1.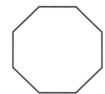

_____

2.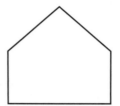

_____

3.

_____

4.

_____

5.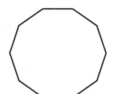

_____

6.

_____

Directions: Now try to classify these unusual shapes!

7.

_____

8.

_____

9.

_____

Practice 7

Lines of Symmetry

Directions: A shape is symmetrical, if when folded in half, both parts overlap exactly. Look at the shapes below. Are they symmetrical?

1.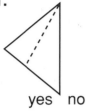

   yes no

2.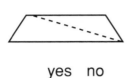

   yes no

3.

   yes no

4.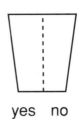

   yes no

5.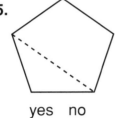

   yes no

6.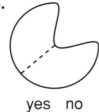

   yes no

7.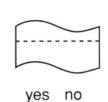

   yes no

8.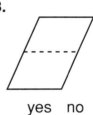

   yes no

Directions: Draw the line of symmetry for each shape.

9.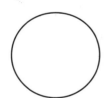

10.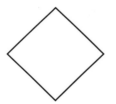

11.

12.

13.

14.

15.

16.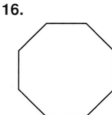

17.

18.

19.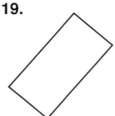

20.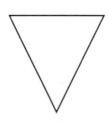

Practice 8

Symmetry

Directions: A shape is symmetrical, if when folded in half, both halves overlap exactly. Cut out (or trace the shapes onto a clean sheet of paper and then cut out the shapes) the shapes and fold them in half. Which shapes are symmetrical?

Sorting Shapes

Directions: Cut out the shapes (or trace them onto a clean sheet of paper). Sort the shapes into different groups. (The shapes can be turned once they have been cut out.)

- by the number of sides
- by the same shapes
- by same size and shapes

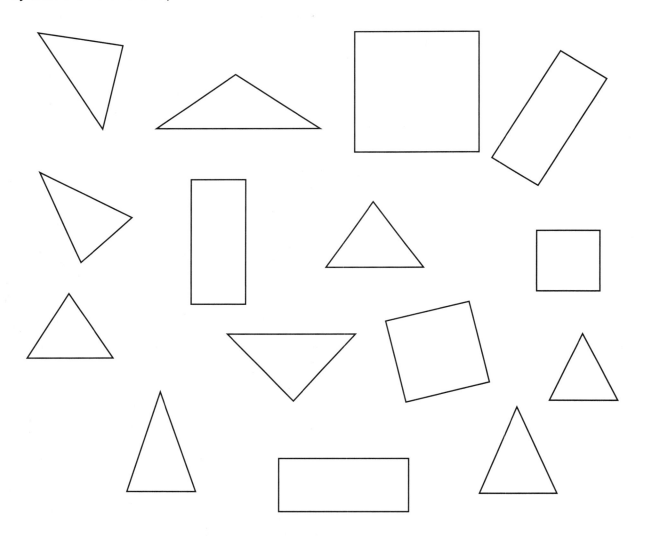

1. Group the items by the number of sides. How many groups did you make? _____

2. Group the items by shape. How many groups did you make? _____

3. Group the items by same size and shape. How many groups did you make? _____

Practice 10

More Than One Line of Symmetry

Directions: Circle the shape in each row that has more than one line of symmetry.

1.

2.

3.

4.

5.

6.

7.

Same Size and Same Shape

Directions: Look at each pair of figures below. Are they the same size and same shape?
Circle *yes* or *no*.

1.
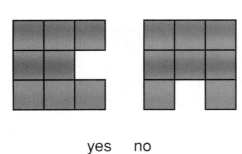

yes   no

2.
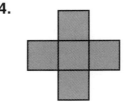

yes   no

3.
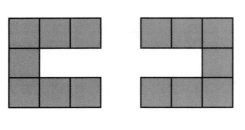

yes   no

4.
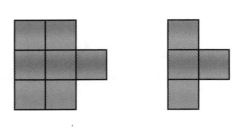

yes   no

5.
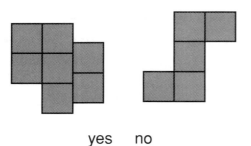

yes   no

6.
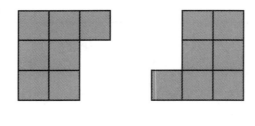

yes   no

7.
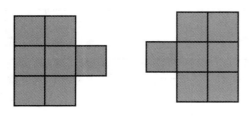

yes   no

8.
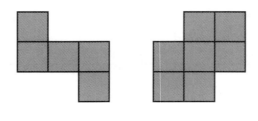

yes   no

Practice 12

Similar or Congruent?

Directions: Are the shapes similar or congruent? (Remember congruent means "the same size and the same shape.")

1. 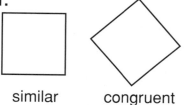 similar congruent	**2.**  similar congruent	**3.**  similar congruent
4. 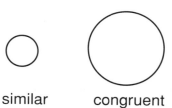 similar congruent	**5.** 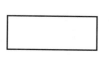 similar congruent	**6.** similar congruent
7. 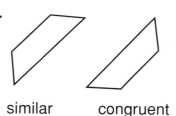 similar congruent	**8.** similar congruent	**9.** similar congruent
10.   similar congruent	**11.** similar congruent	**12.** similar congruent
13.  similar congruent	**14.** similar congruent	**15.**  similar congruent

Practice 13

Count Those Sides and Angles!

> A side is the straight part on a shape.
>
> An angle is formed when two sides meet.

Directions: Count the sides and angles on each shape.

1.

sides: _____

angles: _____

2.

sides: _____

angles: _____

3.

sides: _____

angles: _____

4.

sides: _____

angles: _____

5.

sides: _____

angles: _____

6.

sides: _____

angles: _____

7.

sides: _____

angles: _____

8.

sides: _____

angles: _____

9.

sides: _____

angles: _____

10. What do you notice about the number of sides and angles on each shape? _____

_____

11. Try to draw a shape with a number of angles that is different from the number of sides in the shape.

Practice 14

Right Angles

Right Angles

- Exactly 90°
- Make a square corner means a 90° angle

Samples of right angles:

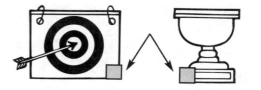

Directions: Identify a right angle in each item below.

1.
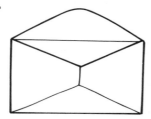

2.
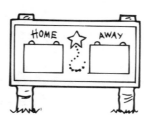

3.

4.
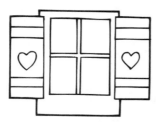

5.

6.

7.

8.
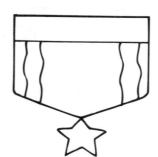

9.
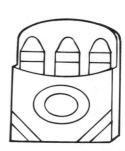

10.
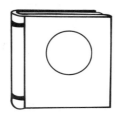

11.

12.
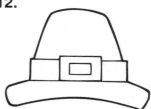

Practice 15

What Is an Angle?

An angle is formed when two lines meet.
The pennant has three angles.   The pencil has five angles.

1. Circle the shapes below that have angles.

There are three different kinds of angles—acute angles, right angles, and obtuse angles.

Acute angles are less than 90°.
Acute angles do not make a square corner.

Right angles are exactly 90°.
Right angles make a square corner.

Obtuse angles are greater than 90°.
Obtuse angles do not make a square corner.

Directions: Identify angle *A* below. Is it an acute angle, a right angle, or an obtuse angle?

2.   **3.**   **4.**

_____   _____   _____

5.   **6.**   **7.**

_____   _____   _____

Practice 16

Identifying Angles

Directions: Identify each angle. Circle the answer.

1.

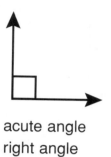

acute angle
right angle
obtuse angle

2.

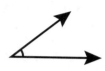

acute angle
right angle
obtuse angle

3.

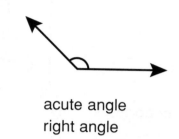

acute angle
right angle
obtuse angle

4.

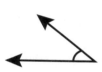

acute angle
right angle
obtuse angle

5.

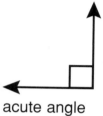

acute angle
right angle
obtuse angle

6.

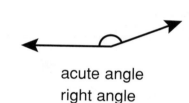

acute angle
right angle
obtuse angle

7.

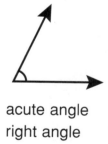

acute angle
right angle
obtuse angle

8.

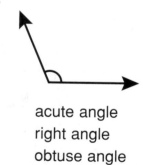

acute angle
right angle
obtuse angle

9.

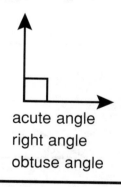

acute angle
right angle
obtuse angle

10. Draw a right angle

11. Draw an acute angle

12. Draw an obtuse angle

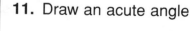

Practice 17

Angles, Angles, Angles

> **Acute angle:** The angle is less than 90°.
>
> **Right angle:** The angle is exactly 90°.
>
> **Obtuse angle:** The angle is greater than 90°.
>
> **Straight angle:** The angle is 180°.

Directions: Identify each kind of angle.

1.

2.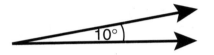

_____

3.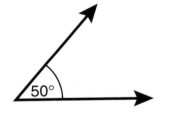

_____

4.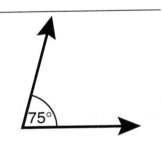

_____

5.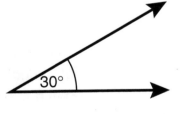

_____

6.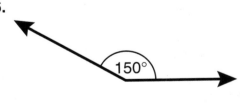

_____

7.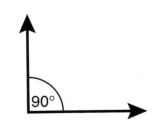

_____

8.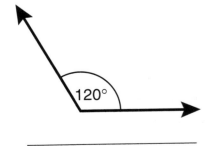

_____

Practice 18

Naming Angles

Directions: Look at the angle marked with an *. What kind of angle is it? Circle the correct answer.

1.

acute angle
right angle
obtuse angle

2.

acute angle
right angle
obtuse angle

3.

acute angle
right angle
obtuse angle

4.

acute angle
right angle
obtuse angle

5.

acute angle
right angle
obtuse angle

6.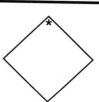

acute angle
right angle
obtuse angle

7.

acute angle
right angle
obtuse angle

8.

acute angle
right angle
obtuse angle

9.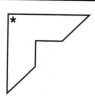

acute angle
right angle
obtuse angle

10.

acute angle
right angle
obtuse angle

11.

acute angle
right angle
obtuse angle

12.

acute angle
right angle
obtuse angle

Triangles: By the Sides

Triangles can be described by the number of **congruent** sides. **Congruent** means the sides are the exactly the same.

Scalene Triangle	Isosceles Triangle	Equilateral Triangle
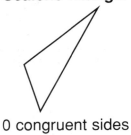		
0 congruent sides	2 congruent sides	3 congruent sides

Directions: Identify each triangle.

1. Number of congruent sides: _____

   Kind of triangle:_____

2. Number of congruent sides: _____

   Kind of triangle:_____

3. Number of congruent sides: _____

   Kind of triangle:_____

4. Number of congruent sides: _____

   Kind of triangle:_____
   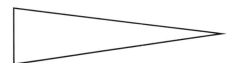

5. Number of congruent sides: _____

   Kind of triangle:_____

6. Number of congruent sides: _____

   Kind of triangle:_____

Practice 20

Triangles: By the Angles

Triangles can be described by their angles. An **angle** is where two sides meet.

- acute angle = one angle is less than 90°
- right angle = one angle is exactly 90°
- obtuse angle = one angle greater than 90°

Acute Triangle	Right Triangle	Obtuse Triangle
3 acute angles	1 right angle	angle greater than 90°

Directions: Name each triangle.

1.

_____

2.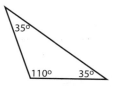

_____

3.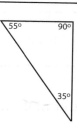

_____

4.

_____

5.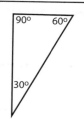

_____

6.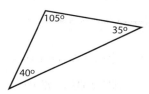

_____

7.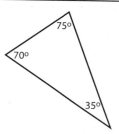

_____

8.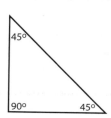

_____

9.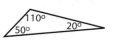

_____

Practice 21

Lines, Line Segments, and Rays

- A **line** is a set of points that stretch endlessly in both directions.

  Symbol for a line: ⟷

- A **line segment** is a set of points on a line. A line segment has a beginning and an end. The beginning and the end are called **end points**. Every line segment is a subset of a line.

  Line:

  Symbol for a line segment: _____

  Naming the line segments: $\overline{AB}$ or $\overline{BA}$

- A ray is another kind of subset of a line. A **ray** is a point on a line and contains all points on the line extending in one direction from that point.

  Symbol for a ray: ⟶

  Naming line segments on a ray:

  The rays are: $\overrightarrow{AB}$ $\overrightarrow{AC}$ $\overrightarrow{BC}$ $\overrightarrow{CB}$ $\overrightarrow{CA}$ $\overrightarrow{BA}$

Directions: Name each line.

1. 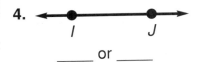   C   D

2. ⟷ E   F

3. ⟷ G   H

Directions: Name each line segment two different ways.

4. ⟷ I   J

_____ or _____

5. ⟷ K   L

_____ or _____

6. ⟷ M   N

_____ or _____

Directions: Name the rays on each line.

7. 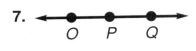   O   P   Q

____   ____

____   ____

____   ____

8.  R   S   T

____   ____

____   ____

____   ____

9. 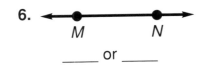 U   V   W

____   ____

____   ____

____   ____

#8600 Practice Makes Perfect: Geometry

Practice 22

Name the Lines, Line Segments, and Rays

Directions: Identify each kind of line.

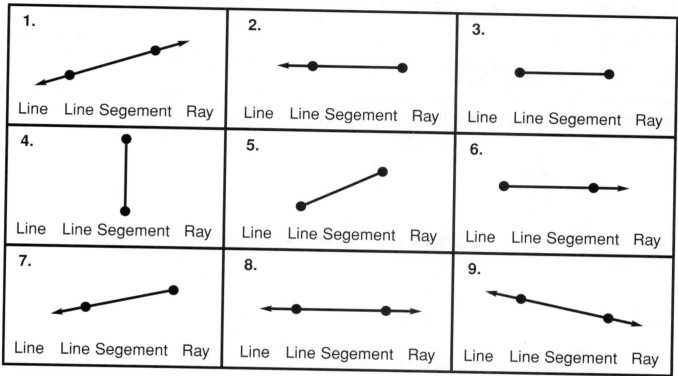

1.

Line   Line Segement   Ray

2.

Line   Line Segement   Ray

3.

Line   Line Segement   Ray

4.

Line   Line Segement   Ray

5.

Line   Line Segement   Ray

6.

Line   Line Segement   Ray

7.

Line   Line Segement   Ray

8.

Line   Line Segement   Ray

9.

Line   Line Segement   Ray

Directions: Draw each kind of line.

10. line with points *A*, *B*, and *C*	**11.** line segment with endpoints *D* and *E*	**12.** ray with points *F* and *G*
13. line with points *H*, *I*, and *J*	**14.** ray with points *K*, *L*, and *M*	**15.** line segment with endpoints *N* and *O*
16. ray with points *P*, *Q*, and *R*	**17.** line with points *S* and *T*	**18.** line segment with endpoints *U* and *V*

Angles

An **angle** is formed when two rays meet.

The **vertex** is the common endpoint of an angle.

Symbol for angle: ∠

vertex B   angle

An angle can be named two ways. The vertex is always the second point indicated.
Example: ∠ABC or ∠CBA

Directions: Name each angle two ways.

1.

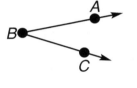

_____ or _____

2.

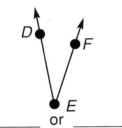

_____ or _____

3.

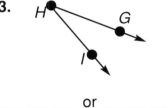

_____ or _____

4.

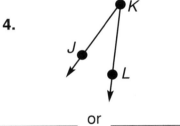

_____ or _____

5.

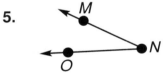

_____ or _____

6.

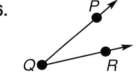

_____ or _____

7. Draw ∠STU.

8. Draw ∠BCD.

9. Draw ∠XYZ.

10. Draw ∠PQR.

11. Draw ∠FGH.

12. Draw ∠LMN.

Practice 24

More About Angles

An **angle** is formed when two rays meet.

The **vertex** is the common endpoint of an angle.

Symbol for angle: $\angle$

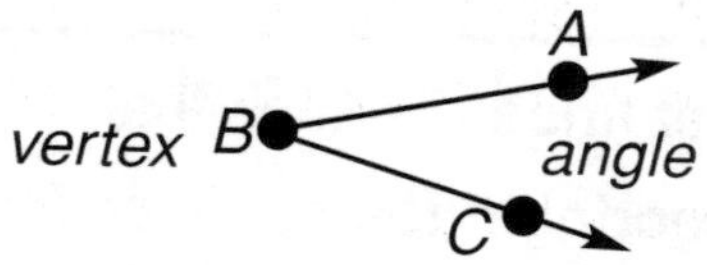

vertex B

A

angle

C

An angle can be named two ways. The vertex is always the second point indicated.
   Example: $\angle ABC$ or $\angle CBA$

Directions: Draw and label the following angles.

1. Draw $\angle STU$.

2. Draw $\angle BCD$.

3. Draw $\angle PQR$.

4. Draw $\angle FGH$.

5. Draw $\angle JKL$.

6. Draw $\angle VWX$.

Practice 25

Parallel Lines and Intersecting Lines

- **Parallel lines** are lines that do not cross each other.
- **Intersecting lines** are lines that cross each other at some point.

Directions: Write *parallel* or *intersecting* on the line.

1.

_____

2.

_____

3.

_____

4.

_____

5.

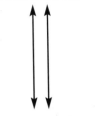

_____

6.

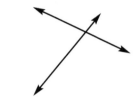

_____

7.

_____

8.

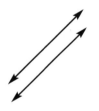

_____

9.

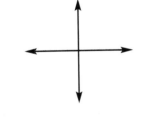

_____

10. Draw a pair of parallel lines.

11. Draw a set of lines that intersect each other.

Practice 26

Perpendicular Lines

Perpendicular lines are two lines that cross each other and form a 90° angle or right angle.

Directions: Are the lines perpendicular? Circle *Yes* or *No*.

1.

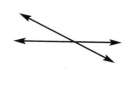

yes   no

2.

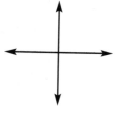

yes   no

3.

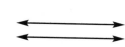

yes   no

4.

yes   no

5.

yes   no

6.

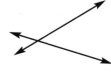

yes   no

7.

yes   no

8.

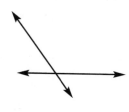

yes   no

9.

yes   no

10.

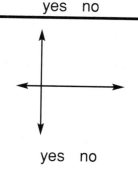

yes   no

11.

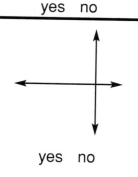

yes   no

12.

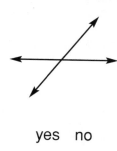

yes   no

13. How are perpendicular lines similar to intersecting lines? _____

_____

14. How are perpendicular lines different from intersecting lines? _____

_____

Practice 27 ⟐ ⟐ ⟐ ⟐ ⟐ ⟐ ⟐ ⟐ ⟐ ⟐ ⟐ ⟐ ⟐ ⟐

More Work with Parallel and Intersecting Lines

Directions: Answer the questions about each set of lines.

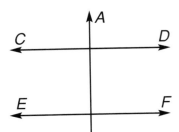

1. $\overleftrightarrow{CD}$ is parallel to which line? _____

2. $\overleftrightarrow{EF}$ is not parallel to which line? _____

3. $\overleftrightarrow{EF}$ is crossed by which line? _____

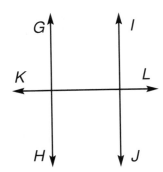

4. $\overleftrightarrow{GH}$ is parallel to which line? _____

5. Name a line that intersects $\overleftrightarrow{KL}$. _____

6. $\overleftrightarrow{IJ}$ is not parallel to which line? _____

Directions: Draw the following lines.

7. Draw $\overleftrightarrow{MN}$ parallel to $\overleftrightarrow{OP}$.

8. Draw $\overleftrightarrow{QR}$ intersecting $\overleftrightarrow{ST}$.

9. Draw $\overleftrightarrow{UV}$ parallel to $\overleftrightarrow{WX}$.
Draw $\overleftrightarrow{YZ}$ intersecting $\overleftrightarrow{UV}$ and $\overleftrightarrow{WX}$.

10. Draw $\overleftrightarrow{AB}$ intersecting $\overleftrightarrow{CD}$.
Draw $\overleftrightarrow{EF}$ parallel to $\overleftrightarrow{CD}$.

Practice 28

Flips and Slides

Directions: A **flip** is when a picture is turned over. A **slide** is when the picture is moved over. Look at each pair of pictures. To go from the first picture to the second picture, was it flipped or did it slide?

1. flip   slide

2. flip   slide

3. flip   slide

4. flip   slide

5. flip   slide

6. flip   slide

7. flip   slide

8. flip   slide

9. flip   slide

Directions: What comes next in each pattern?

10.

11.

12.

13.

Practice 29

Twists and Turns

An object can be rotated **clockwise** by degrees (or in other words—turned!).

Start	90° ¼ turn	180° ½ turn	270° ¾ turn	360° full turn

Directions: To what degree was each item turned? Circle the answer.

1. 90° 180° 270° 360°	**2.** 90° 180° 270° 360°	**3.** 90° 180° 270° 360°
4. 90° 180° 270° 360°	**5.** 90° 180° 270° 360°	**6.** 90° 180° 270° 360°
7. 90° 180° 270° 360°	**8.** 90° 180° 270° 360°	**9.** 90° 180° 270° 360°
10. 90° 180° 270° 360°	**11.** 90° 180° 270° 360°	**12.** 90° 180° 270° 360°
13. 90° 180° 270° 360°	**14.** 90° 180° 270° 360°	**15.** 90° 180° 270° 360°

#8600 Practice Makes Perfect: Geometry   © *Teacher Created Resources, Inc.*

Practice 30

Parts of a Solid

Solids have three parts.

- **Face:** the flat surfaces
- **Edge:** where two faces meet
- **Vertex:** corner where three edges meet
- **Curved:** the surface is rounded, not flat

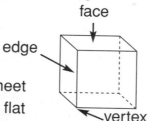

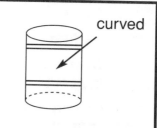

Directions: Count the number of flat surfaces, curved surfaces, edges, and vertices on each solid.

1.

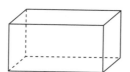

flat surfaces: _____
curved surfaces: _____
edges: _____
vertices: _____

2.

flat surfaces: _____
curved surfaces: _____
edges: _____
vertices: _____

3.

flat surfaces: _____
curved surfaces: _____
edges: _____
vertices: _____

4.

flat surfaces: _____
curved surfaces: _____
edges: _____
vertices: _____

5.

flat surfaces: _____
curved surfaces: _____
edges: _____
vertices: _____

6.

flat surfaces: _____
curved surfaces: _____
edges: _____
vertices: _____

7.

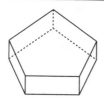

flat surfaces: _____
curved surfaces: _____
edges: _____
vertices: _____

8.

flat surfaces: _____
curved surfaces: _____
edges: _____
vertices: _____

9.

flat surfaces: _____
curved surfaces: _____
edges: _____
vertices: _____

Practice 31

Circles

- **Center:** middle of the circle
- **Radius:** distance from the center of the circle to any point on the side of the circle
- **Diameter:** distance from one side of the circle to the opposite side going through the center
- **Circumference:** distance around the circle

Directions: Name the part of the circle to which the arrow is pointing.

1.

2.

3.

_____

_____

_____

4.

5.

6.

_____

_____

_____

Directions: The diameter *(d)* is twice the length of the radius *(r)*. What is the diameter of each circle?

7.
r = 3 in.

8.
r = 4 in.

9.
r = 2 in.

d = _____ in.

d = _____ in.

d = _____ in.

Directions: The radius *(r)* is half the length of the diameter *(d)*. What is the radius of each circle?

10.
d = 8 in.

11.
d = 10 in.

12.
d = 6 in.

r = _____ in.

r = _____ in.

r = _____ in.

Practice 32

Perimeter

Directions: The perimeter *(P)* is the area around the outside of the shape. To find the perimeter, add all of the sides of the shape together.

1.
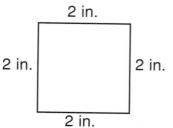

2 in.
2 in.   2 in.
2 in.

P = _____ in.

2.
4 in.
3 in.   3 in.
4 in.

P = _____ in.

3.
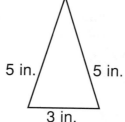

5 in.   5 in.
3 in.

P = _____ in.

4.
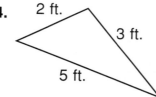

2 ft.
3 ft.
5 ft.

P = _____ ft.

5.
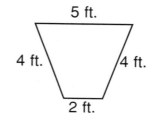

5 ft.
4 ft.   4 ft.
2 ft.

P = _____ ft.

6.
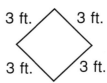

3 ft.   3 ft.
3 ft.   3 ft.

P = _____ ft.

7.
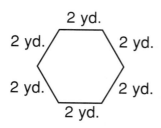

2 yd.
2 yd.   2 yd.
2 yd.   2 yd.
2 yd.

P = _____ yd.

8.
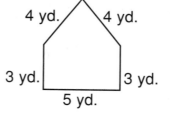

4 yd.   4 yd.
3 yd.   3 yd.
5 yd.

P = _____ yd.

9.
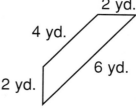

2 yd.
4 yd.
6 yd.
2 yd.

P = _____ yd.

10.
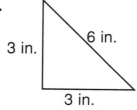

3 in.   6 in.
3 in.

P = _____ in.

11.
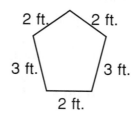

2 ft.   2 ft.
3 ft.   3 ft.
2 ft.

P = _____ ft.

12.
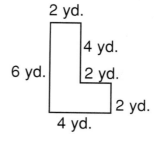

2 yd.
4 yd.
6 yd.   2 yd.
2 yd.
4 yd.

P = _____ yd.

Practice 33

Finding the Area of Squares and Rectangles

To find the area of a square or rectangle, multiply the length by the width.

Formula: Area = length x width = square units $A = l \times w$ = sq. units

Directions: Find the area for each square and rectangle.

1.

3 in.

3 in.

_____ x _____ = _____ sq. in.

2.

7 in.

1 in.

_____ x _____ = _____ sq. in.

3.

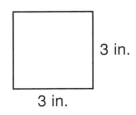

5 in.

5 in.

_____ x _____ = _____ sq. in.

4.

3 in.

4 in.

_____ x _____ = _____ sq. in.

5.

3 ft.

1 ft.

_____ x _____ = _____ sq. ft.

6.

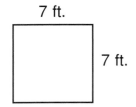

7 ft.

7 ft.

_____ x _____ = _____ sq. ft.

7. What are the dimensions of a square with an area of 36 square inches? _____

8. What are the dimensions of a rectangle with an area of 40 square inches? _____

9. Would a square or a rectangle have an area of 50 square inches? _____

What would its measurements be? _____ x _____

Practice 34

Area of a Triangle

To find the area of a triangle, multiply the base *(b)* by the height *(h)* and divide by 2.

Formula: Area = $\frac{\text{base} \times \text{height}}{2}$ = square units $A = \frac{b \times h}{2}$ = sq. units

Directions: Find the area for each triangle.

1.

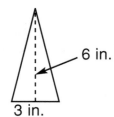

3 in.   6 in.

_____ sq. in.

2.

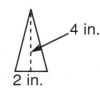

2 in.   4 in.

_____ sq. in.

3.

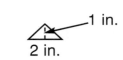

2 in.   1 in.

_____ sq. in.

4.

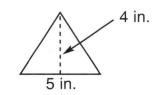

5 in.   4 in.

_____ sq. in.

5.

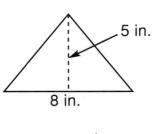

8 in.   5 in.

_____ sq. in.

6.

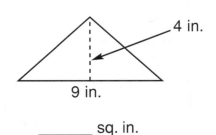

9 in.   4 in.

_____ sq. in.

7. Make a triangle with an area of 12 sq. in.   8. Make a triangle with an area of 15 sq. in.

Practice 35

Area of a Parallelogram

Directions: To find the area of a parallelogram, multiply the base by the height. Measure the base and height of each parallelogram to the nearest centimeter. Find the area.

Formula
$A = b \times h$ = sq. units

1.

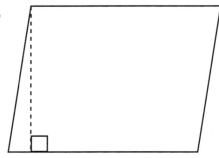

base = _____ height = _____

_____ sq. cm

2.

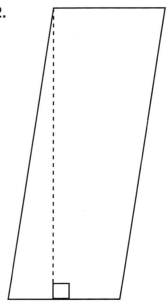

base = _____ height = _____

_____ sq. cm

3.

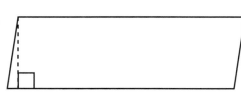

base = _____ height = _____

_____ sq. cm

4.

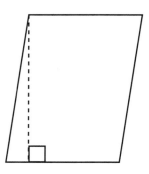

base = _____ height = _____

_____ sq. cm

5.

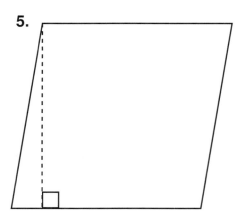

base = _____ height = _____

_____ sq. cm

Practice 36

Volume of a Cube or a Rectangular Prism

Formula for a Cube	Formula for a Rectangular Prism
Volume = side x side x side = cubic units $V = s^3$ = cu. units	Volume = length x width x height = cubic units $V = l$ x w x h = cu. units

Directions: Measure each cube or rectangle to the nearest centimeter. Find the volume for each solid.

1.

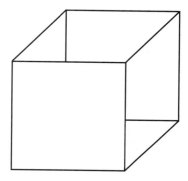

s = _____ cm

_____ x _____ x _____ = _____ cu. cm

2.

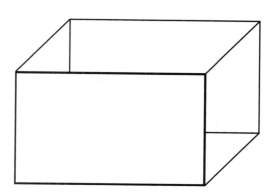

l = _____ cm w = _____ cm h = _____ cm

_____ x _____ x _____ = _____ cu. cm

3.

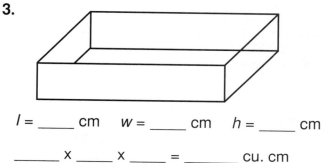

l = _____ cm w = _____ cm h = _____ cm

_____ x _____ x _____ = _____ cu. cm

4.

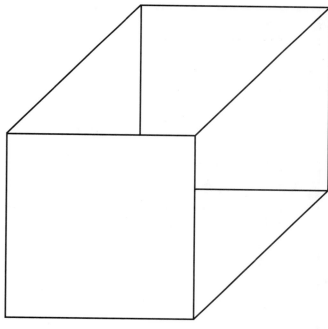

s = _____ cm

_____ x _____ x _____ = _____ cu. cm

Test Practice 1

Directions: Fill in the circle under the correct answer.

1. Name the shape.	2. Name the solid shape.	3. Identify the quadrilateral.
square triangle rectangle	square cube sphere	A B C
Ⓐ Ⓑ Ⓒ	Ⓐ Ⓑ Ⓒ	Ⓐ Ⓑ Ⓒ

4. Identify the pair of shapes that shows a plane shape and its matching solid shape.

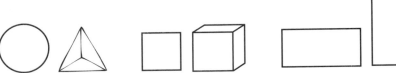

    Ⓐ   Ⓑ   Ⓒ

5. Which statement describes a rectangle?

Ⓐ   4 sides of equal length

Ⓑ   opposite sides of equal length

Ⓒ   4 sides of different lengths

6. Name the plane figure shown on this solid shape.	7. Name the solid shape.	8. Identify the shape that can be made with the pattern.

oval circle square	cone rectangular prism sphere	rectangular prism cube triangular prism
Ⓐ Ⓑ Ⓒ	Ⓐ Ⓑ Ⓒ	Ⓐ Ⓑ Ⓒ

9. Identify the quadrilateral.	10. Which one is a polygon?	11. Identify the polygon.
diamond rhombus triangle	A B C	hexagon heptagon octagon
Ⓐ Ⓑ Ⓒ	Ⓐ Ⓑ Ⓒ	Ⓐ Ⓑ Ⓒ

Test Practice 2

Directions: Fill in the circle under the correct answer.

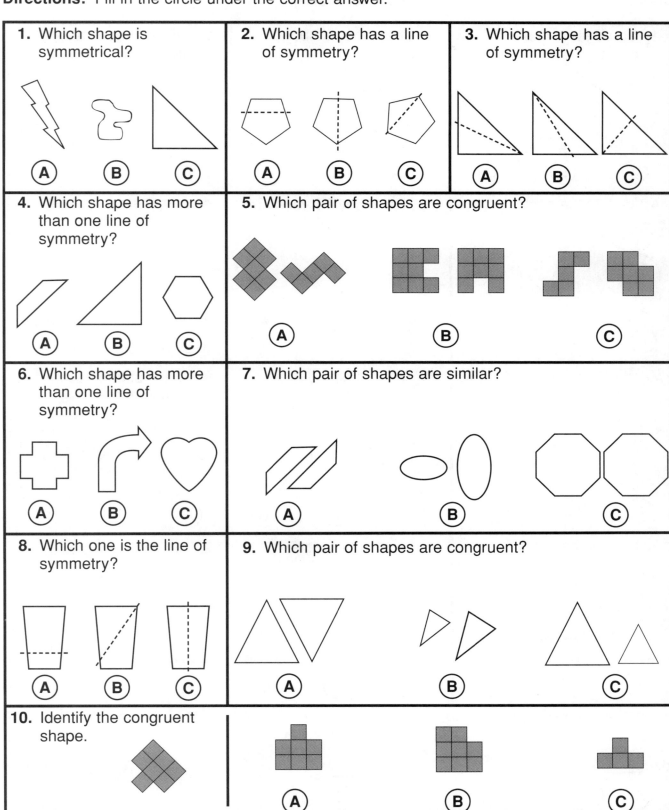

1. Which shape is symmetrical?

Ⓐ Ⓑ Ⓒ

2. Which shape has a line of symmetry?

Ⓐ Ⓑ Ⓒ

3. Which shape has a line of symmetry?

Ⓐ Ⓑ Ⓒ

4. Which shape has more than one line of symmetry?

Ⓐ Ⓑ Ⓒ

5. Which pair of shapes are congruent?

Ⓐ Ⓑ Ⓒ

6. Which shape has more than one line of symmetry?

Ⓐ Ⓑ Ⓒ

7. Which pair of shapes are similar?

Ⓐ Ⓑ Ⓒ

8. Which one is the line of symmetry?

Ⓐ Ⓑ Ⓒ

9. Which pair of shapes are congruent?

Ⓐ Ⓑ Ⓒ

10. Identify the congruent shape.

Ⓐ Ⓑ Ⓒ

Test Practice 3

Directions: Fill in the circle under the correct answer.

1. Count the number of sides.	2. Count the number of sides.	3. Which shape has an angle?
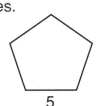		
4 5 6	12 11 10	
Ⓐ Ⓑ Ⓒ	Ⓐ Ⓑ Ⓒ	Ⓐ Ⓑ Ⓒ

4. Identify the angle.	5. How many degrees are in a right angle?	6. Which angle has more than 90°?
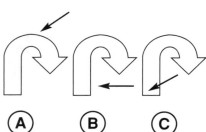		
	< 90° = 90° > 90°	acute right obtuse
Ⓐ Ⓑ Ⓒ	Ⓐ Ⓑ Ⓒ	Ⓐ Ⓑ Ⓒ

7. Which shape has a right angle?	8. Which shape has an acute angle?	9. Which shape has an obtuse angle?
	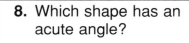	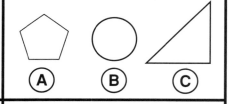
Ⓐ Ⓑ Ⓒ	Ⓐ Ⓑ Ⓒ	Ⓐ Ⓑ Ⓒ

10. Identify the angle.	11. Identify the angle.	12. Identify the angle.
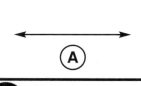	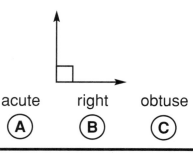	
acute right obtuse	acute right obtuse	acute right obtuse
Ⓐ Ⓑ Ⓒ	Ⓐ Ⓑ Ⓒ	Ⓐ Ⓑ Ⓒ

13. Which one is a straight angle?

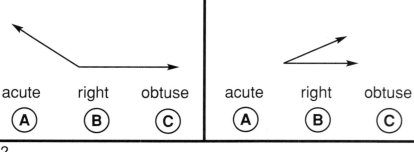

Ⓐ   Ⓑ   Ⓒ

Test Practice 4

Directions: Fill in the circle under the correct answer.

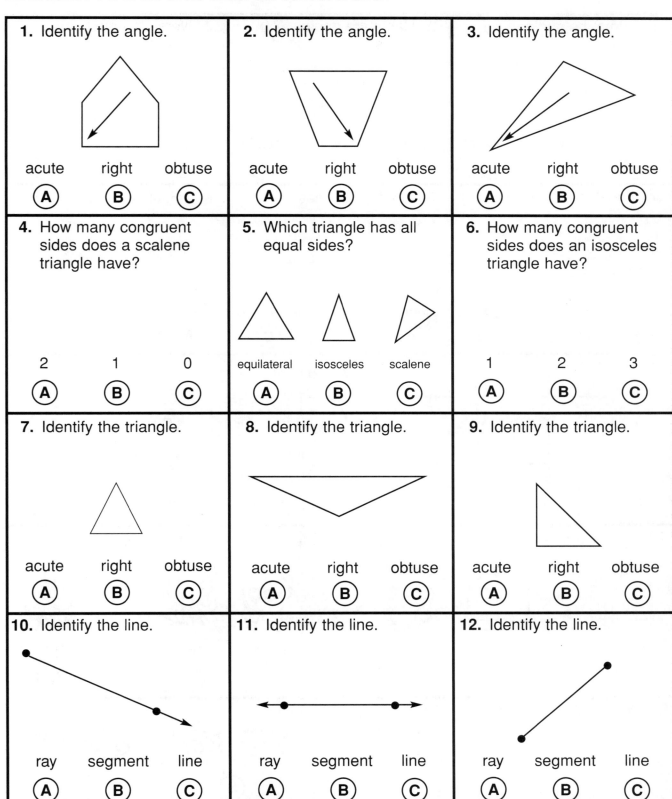

1. Identify the angle.

acute   right   obtuse
(A)   (B)   (C)

2. Identify the angle.

acute   right   obtuse
(A)   (B)   (C)

3. Identify the angle.

acute   right   obtuse
(A)   (B)   (C)

4. How many congruent sides does a scalene triangle have?

2   1   0
(A)   (B)   (C)

5. Which triangle has all equal sides?

equilateral   isosceles   scalene
(A)   (B)   (C)

6. How many congruent sides does an isosceles triangle have?

1   2   3
(A)   (B)   (C)

7. Identify the triangle.

acute   right   obtuse
(A)   (B)   (C)

8. Identify the triangle.

acute   right   obtuse
(A)   (B)   (C)

9. Identify the triangle.

acute   right   obtuse
(A)   (B)   (C)

10. Identify the line.

ray   segment   line
(A)   (B)   (C)

11. Identify the line.

ray   segment   line
(A)   (B)   (C)

12. Identify the line.

ray   segment   line
(A)   (B)   (C)

Test Practice 5

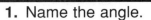

Directions: Fill in the circle under the correct answer.

1. Name the angle. 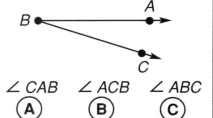 ∠ CAB Ⓐ ∠ ACB Ⓑ ∠ ABC Ⓒ	**2.** Name the angle. 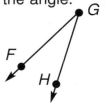 ∠ FGH Ⓐ ∠ HFG Ⓑ ∠ GFH Ⓒ	**3.** Name the angle. 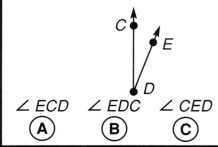 ∠ ECD Ⓐ ∠ EDC Ⓑ ∠ CED Ⓒ

4. Identify the lines.  parallel Ⓐ intersecting Ⓑ perpendicular Ⓒ	**5.** Identify the lines. 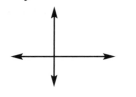 parallel Ⓐ intersecting Ⓑ perpendicular Ⓒ	**6.** Identify the lines. 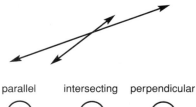 parallel Ⓐ intersecting Ⓑ perpendicular Ⓒ

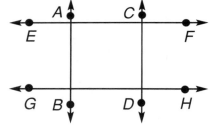

7. $\overline{AB}$ is parallel to _____.

$\overline{EF}$ Ⓐ $\overline{GH}$ Ⓑ $\overline{CD}$ Ⓒ

8. $\overline{EF}$ intersects _____.

$\overline{AB}$ Ⓐ $\overline{GH}$ Ⓑ $\overline{EF}$ Ⓒ

9. Is it a flip or slide? 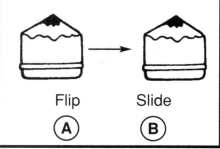 Flip Ⓐ Slide Ⓑ	**10.** Is it a flip or slide? Flip Ⓐ Slide Ⓑ	**11.** Identify the turn. 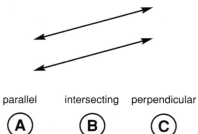 90° Ⓐ 180° Ⓑ 270° Ⓒ

12. Which pair of pictures shows a 360° turn?

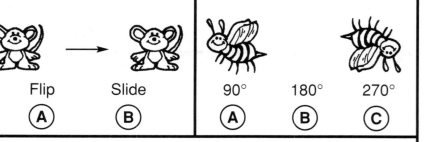

Ⓐ   Ⓑ   Ⓒ

Test Practice 6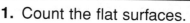

Directions: Fill in the circle under the correct answer.

1. Count the flat surfaces. 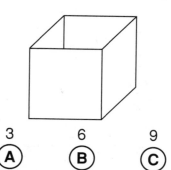 3 6 9 Ⓐ Ⓑ Ⓒ	**2.** Count the curved surfaces.  0 2 1 Ⓐ Ⓑ Ⓒ	**3.** Count the vertices. 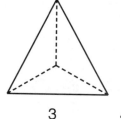 2 3 4 Ⓐ Ⓑ Ⓒ
4. Identify the part of the circle. center radius diameter Ⓐ Ⓑ Ⓒ	**5.** Identify the part of the circle. 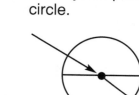 center radius diameter Ⓐ Ⓑ Ⓒ	**6.** Identify the part of the circle. 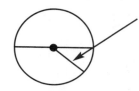 center radius diameter Ⓐ Ⓑ Ⓒ
7. Find the perimeter. 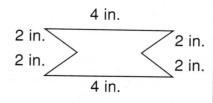 16 in. 8 in. 10 in. Ⓐ Ⓑ Ⓒ	**8.** Find the perimeter. 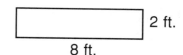 16 feet 18 feet 20 feet Ⓐ Ⓑ Ⓒ	**9.** Find the area. 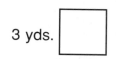 6 square yards 9 square yards 12 square yards Ⓐ Ⓑ Ⓒ
10. Find the area of this triangle. 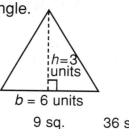 $h=3$ units $b=6$ units 18 sq. units 9 sq. units 36 sq. units Ⓐ Ⓑ Ⓒ	**11.** Find the area of this parallelogram. $h=4$ units $b=5$ units 9 sq. units 25 sq. units 20 sq. units Ⓐ Ⓑ Ⓒ	**12.** Find the volume. 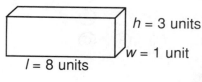 $h=3$ units $w=1$ unit $l=8$ units 13 cu. units 24 cu. units 16 cu. units Ⓐ Ⓑ Ⓒ

Answer Sheet

Test Practice 1	Test Practice 2	Test Practice 3
1. Ⓐ Ⓑ Ⓒ	1. Ⓐ Ⓑ Ⓒ	1. Ⓐ Ⓑ Ⓒ
2. Ⓐ Ⓑ Ⓒ	2. Ⓐ Ⓑ Ⓒ	2. Ⓐ Ⓑ Ⓒ
3. Ⓐ Ⓑ Ⓒ	3. Ⓐ Ⓑ Ⓒ	3. Ⓐ Ⓑ Ⓒ
4. Ⓐ Ⓑ Ⓒ	4. Ⓐ Ⓑ Ⓒ	4. Ⓐ Ⓑ Ⓒ
5. Ⓐ Ⓑ Ⓒ	5. Ⓐ Ⓑ Ⓒ	5. Ⓐ Ⓑ Ⓒ
6. Ⓐ Ⓑ Ⓒ	6. Ⓐ Ⓑ Ⓒ	6. Ⓐ Ⓑ Ⓒ
7. Ⓐ Ⓑ Ⓒ	7. Ⓐ Ⓑ Ⓒ	7. Ⓐ Ⓑ Ⓒ
8. Ⓐ Ⓑ Ⓒ	8. Ⓐ Ⓑ Ⓒ	8. Ⓐ Ⓑ Ⓒ
9. Ⓐ Ⓑ Ⓒ	9. Ⓐ Ⓑ Ⓒ	9. Ⓐ Ⓑ Ⓒ
10. Ⓐ Ⓑ Ⓒ	10. Ⓐ Ⓑ Ⓒ	10. Ⓐ Ⓑ Ⓒ
11. Ⓐ Ⓑ Ⓒ		11. Ⓐ Ⓑ Ⓒ
		12. Ⓐ Ⓑ Ⓒ
		13. Ⓐ Ⓑ Ⓒ

Test Practice 4	Test Practice 5	Test Practice 6
1. Ⓐ Ⓑ Ⓒ	1. Ⓐ Ⓑ Ⓒ	1. Ⓐ Ⓑ Ⓒ
2. Ⓐ Ⓑ Ⓒ	2. Ⓐ Ⓑ Ⓒ	2. Ⓐ Ⓑ Ⓒ
3. Ⓐ Ⓑ Ⓒ	3. Ⓐ Ⓑ Ⓒ	3. Ⓐ Ⓑ Ⓒ
4. Ⓐ Ⓑ Ⓒ	4. Ⓐ Ⓑ Ⓒ	4. Ⓐ Ⓑ Ⓒ
5. Ⓐ Ⓑ Ⓒ	5. Ⓐ Ⓑ Ⓒ	5. Ⓐ Ⓑ Ⓒ
6. Ⓐ Ⓑ Ⓒ	6. Ⓐ Ⓑ Ⓒ	6. Ⓐ Ⓑ Ⓒ
7. Ⓐ Ⓑ Ⓒ	7. Ⓐ Ⓑ Ⓒ	7. Ⓐ Ⓑ Ⓒ
8. Ⓐ Ⓑ Ⓒ	8. Ⓐ Ⓑ Ⓒ	8. Ⓐ Ⓑ Ⓒ
9. Ⓐ Ⓑ Ⓒ	9. Ⓐ Ⓑ	9. Ⓐ Ⓑ Ⓒ
10. Ⓐ Ⓑ Ⓒ	10. Ⓐ Ⓑ	10. Ⓐ Ⓑ Ⓒ
11. Ⓐ Ⓑ Ⓒ	11. Ⓐ Ⓑ Ⓒ	11. Ⓐ Ⓑ Ⓒ
12. Ⓐ Ⓑ Ⓒ	12. Ⓐ Ⓑ Ⓒ	12. Ⓐ Ⓑ Ⓒ

Answer Key

Page 4
1. square matched to cube, triangle matched to triangular pyramid, circle matched to sphere, rectangle matched to rectangular prism
2. rectangle and square
3. triangle and rectangle
4. square
5. circle
6. circle
7. triangle

Page 5
1. sphere
2. cylinder
3. cone
4. cone
5. rectangular prism
6. pyramid
7. cylinder
8. cylinder
9. rectangular prism
10. Sample answer: A soda can is shaped like a cylinder.

Page 6
1. cube
2. rectangular pyramid
3. rectangular prism
4. triangular pyramid
5. cone
6. cylinder

Page 7
Check to make sure that the student has made hash marks on the congruent sides.
1. square
2. rectangle
3. square
4. rectangle
5. square
6. rectangle
Sample answers:
7. They both have angles that are exactly 90 degrees.
8. A square has all four sides of equal length. A rectangle has opposite sides of equal length.

Page 8
1. Circle
2. Circle
4. Circle
5.–10. Check to make sure the students have marked the parallel sides.
5. trapezoid
6. parallelogram
7. rhombus
8. rhombus
9. trapezoid
10. parallelogram

Sample answers
11. They both have four sides.
12. A rectangle has two pairs of parallel sides. A trapezoid has only one pair of parallel sides.

Page 9
1. octagon
2. pentagon
3. hexagon
4. heptagon
5. decagon
6. nonagon
7. hexagon
8. heptagon
9. decagon

Page 10
1. no
2. no
3. yes
4. yes
5. no
6. yes
7. no
8. no
9.–20. Check to make sure that the student has correctly drawn the line of symmetry on each shape.

Page 11
The arrow and "starburst" shape are not symmetrical.

Page 12
1. 2   2. 3   3. 11

Page 13
1. arrow
2. hexagon
3. octagon
4. square
5. triangle
6. rectangle
7. diamond

Page 14
1. Yes   5. No
2. No   6. Yes
3. Yes   7. Yes
4. Yes   8. No

Page 15
1. Congruent
2. Similar
3. Congruent
4. Similar
5. Congruent
6. Similar
7. Congruent
8. Similar
9. Congruent
10. Congruent

11. Similar
12. Congruent
13. Similar
14. Similar
15. Congruent

Page 16
1. 4, 4   6. 6, 6
2. 3, 3   7. 10, 10
3. 5, 5   8. 6, 6,
4. 10, 10   9. 8, 8
5. 4, 4
Sample answers:
10. They are the same number.
11. I cannot because there are always the same number of angles as sides.

Page 17
Check to make sure that the student has identified a right angle on each item.

Page 18
1. Circle the triangle, trapezoid, and cross.
2. right angle
3. acute angle
4. obtuse angle
5. obtuse angle
6. right angle
7. acute angle

Page 19
1. right angle
2. acute angle
3. obtuse angle
4. acute angle
5. right angle
6. obtuse angle
7. acute angle
8. obtuse angle
9. right angle
10.–12. Check to make sure the student has drawn each angle correctly.

Page 20
1. straight angle
2. acute angle
3. acute angle
4. acute angle
5. acute angle
6. obtuse angle
7. right angle
8. obtuse angle

Page 21
1. right angle
2. acute angle
3. acute angle
4. obtuse angle
5. obtuse angle
6. right angle
7. right angle
8. obtuse angle
9. obtuse angle
10. right angle

11. obtuse angle
12. right angle

Page 22
1. 0, scalene
2. 2, isosceles
3. 3, equilateral
4. 0, scalene
5. 3, equilateral
6. 2, isosceles

Page 23
1. right triangle
2. right triangle
3. obtuse triangle
4. obtuse triangle
5. right triangle
6. right triangle
7. acute triangle
8. right triangle
9. obtuse triangle

Page 24
1. $\overleftrightarrow{CD}$ or $\overleftrightarrow{DC}$
2. $\overleftrightarrow{EF}$ or $\overleftrightarrow{FE}$
3. $\overleftrightarrow{GH}$ or $\overleftrightarrow{HG}$
4. $\overline{IJ}$ or $\overline{JI}$
5. $\overline{KL}$ or $\overline{LK}$
6. $\overline{MN}$ or $\overline{NM}$
7. $\overrightarrow{OP}, \overrightarrow{OQ}, \overrightarrow{PQ}, \overrightarrow{QP}, \overrightarrow{QO}, \overrightarrow{PO}$
8. $\overrightarrow{RS}, \overrightarrow{TS}, \overrightarrow{RT}, \overrightarrow{TR}, \overrightarrow{ST}, \overrightarrow{SR}$
9. $\overrightarrow{UV}, \overrightarrow{WV}, \overrightarrow{UW}, \overrightarrow{WU}, \overrightarrow{VW}, \overrightarrow{VU}$

Page 25
1. Line   6. Ray
2. Ray   7. Ray
3. Line Segment 8. Line
4. Line Segment 9. Line
5. Line Segment
Sample answers:

10. line with points A, B and C	11. line segment with endpoints D and E	12. ray with points F and G
A B C	D E	F G
13. line with segments H, I, and J	14. ray with points K, L, and M	15. line segment with endpoints N and O
H I J	K L M	N O
16. ray with points P, Q, and R	17. line with points S and T	18. line segment with endpoints U and V
P Q R	S T	U V

Page 26
1. $\angle ABC, \angle CBA$
2. $\angle DEF, \angle FED$
3. $\angle GHI, \angle IHG$
4. $\angle JKL, \angle LKJ$
5. $\angle MNO, \angle ONM$
6. $\angle PQR, \angle RQP$
7.–12. Check to make sure the student has labeled the angles correctly.

Answer Key

Page 27
1.–6. Check to make sure the student has labeled the angles correctly.

Page 28
1. parallel
2. intersecting
3. parallel
4. parallel
5. parallel
6. intersecting
7. intersecting
8. parallel
9. intersecting
10.–11. Check to make sure the student has drawn the lines correctly.

Page 29
1. No
2. Yes
3. No
4. No
5. Yes
6. No
7. No
8. No
9. No
10. Yes
11. Yes
12. No
13. They both cross another line.
14. An intersecting line crosses another line. A perpendicular line crosses another line to form a 90 degree angle.

Page 30
1. $\overleftrightarrow{EF}$
2. $\overrightarrow{AB}$
3. $\overleftrightarrow{AB}$
4. $\overleftrightarrow{IJ}$
5. $\overleftrightarrow{GH}$ or $\overleftrightarrow{IJ}$
6. $\overleftrightarrow{KL}$

Sample Answers:

7. Draw $\overrightarrow{MN}$ parallel to $\overrightarrow{OP}$.

8. Draw $\overrightarrow{QR}$ intersecting $\overrightarrow{ST}$.

9. Draw $\overrightarrow{UV}$ parallel to $\overrightarrow{WX}$.
Draw $\overrightarrow{YZ}$ intersecting $\overrightarrow{UV}$ and $\overrightarrow{WX}$.

10. Draw $\overrightarrow{AB}$ intersecting $\overrightarrow{CD}$.
Draw $\overrightarrow{EF}$ parallel to $\overrightarrow{CD}$.

Page 31
1. Slide
2. Flip
3. Flip
4. Flip
5. Slide
6. Flip
7. Flip
8. Slide
9. Flip
10. first car
11. second stadium
12. first dog
13. first alien

Page 32
1. 90°
2. 180°
3. 360°
4. 360°
5. 180°
6. 270°
7. 180°
8. 360°
9. 180°
10. 90°
11. 180°
12. 270°
13. 360°
14. 180°
15. 90°

Page 33
1. 6, 0, 12, 8
2. 5, 0, 8, 5
3. 2, 1, 2, 0
4. 1, 1, 1, 1
5. 6, 0, 12, 8
6. 0, 1, 0, 0
7. 7, 0, 15, 10
8. 8, 0, 18, 12
9. 4, 0, 6, 4

Page 34
1. radius
2. center
3. diameter
4. radius
5. diameter
6. circumference
7. 6 in.
8. 8 in.
9. 4 in.
10. 4 in.
11. 5 in.
12. 3 in.

Page 35
1. 8 in.
2. 14 in.
3. 13 in.
4. 10 ft.
5. 15 ft.
6. 12 ft.
7. 12 yd.
8. 19 yd.
9. 14 yd.
10. 12 in.
11. 12 ft.
12. 20 yd.

Page 36
1. 3 x 3 = 9 sq. in.
2. 7 x 1 = 7 sq. in.
3. 5 x 5 = 25 sq. in.
4. 4 x 3 = 12 sq. in.
5. 3 x 1 = 3 sq. in.
6. 7 x 7 = 49 sq. ft.
7. 6 inches x 6 inches
8. Possibe answers:
    2 inches x 20 inches,
    8 inches x 5 inches
9. rectangle, 10 inches x 5 inches

Page 37
1. 9 sq. in.
2. 4 sq. in.
3. 1 sq. in.
4. 10 sq. in.
5. 20 sq. in.
6. 18 sq. in.
Sample answers:
7. base of 6 in., height of 4 in.
8. base of 6 in., height of 5 in.

Page 38
1. base = 5 cm
    height = 4 cm
    20 sq. cm
2. base = 3 cm
    height = 8 cm
    24 sq. cm
3. base = 6 cm
    height 2 cm
    12 sq. cm
4. base = 3 cm
    height = 4 cm
    12 sq. cm
5. base = 5 cm
    height = 5 cm
    25 sq. cm

Page 39
1. s = 3 cm
    3 x 3 x 3 = 27 cu. cm
2. l = 5 cm, w = 2 cm,
    h = 3 cm
    5 x 2 x 3 = 30 cu. cm
3. l = 5 cm, w = 2 cm,
    h = 1 cm
    5 x 2 x 1 = 10 cu. cm
4. s = 5 cm
    5 x 5 x 5 = 125 cu. cm

Page 40
1. B
2. C
3. C
4. B
5. B
6. B
7. A
8. A
9. B
10. B
11. C

Page 41
1. C
2. B
3. C
4. C
5. B
6. A
7. B
8. C
9. A
10. A

Page 42
1. B
2. A
3. C
4. C
5. B
6. C
7. B
8. A
9. A
10. B
11. C
12. A
13. A

Page 43
1. B
2. C
3. A
4. C
5. A
6. B
7. A
8. C
9. B
10. A
11. C
12. B

Page 44
1. C
2. A
3. B
4. B
5. C or B
6. A
7. C
8. A
9. B
10. B
11. B
12. B

Page 45
1. B
2. C
3. C
4. C
5. A
6. B
7. A
8. C
9. B
10. B
11. C
12. B